THE GREENWICH MERIDIAN

Stuart Malin
Carole Stott

ORDNANCE SURVEY
SOUTHAMPTON

THE GREENWICH MERIDIAN

Greenwich is known all over the World because of its meridian which is universally used for timekeeping and navigation on land, at sea and in the air. Even astronauts use Greenwich Mean Time. Why was this meridian chosen as zero longitude, dividing East from West? Why not the line through the Pyramids or New York? The reasons are largely historical and involve a king's mistress, railway timetables, the man who weighed the Earth and a prize of £20 000.

Here, we tell the story of the Greenwich Meridian, answering the questions where? what? why? and how? First we describe where it goes, with special emphasis on Great Britain, then we explain how longitude, time and maps all depend on the Meridian. Next comes the history of the Royal Observatory at Greenwich and the adoption of the line through one of its telescopes as the prime meridian of the World. Finally, we describe the instruments that define the Meridian and help to determine longitude and time.

Second Edition
© *Crown Copyright 1989*

ISBN 0 319 00191 1

ONE

North Pole to South Pole

Noah's Ark, Orwell, 1984 and the Patrington Windmill all have something in common. The link has nothing to do with George Orwell and his famous novel *1984*. The answer is that Noah's Ark, Orwell and the windmill all lie on the Greenwich Meridian; the Meridian that celebrated its centenary in 1984 as zero longitude for the World. These places are all in England but the question could have easily been, what do Lourdes, the Western Sahara and the Gulf of Valencia have in common? Like any other meridian, that through Greenwich joins the North and South Poles. As the World's chosen prime meridian it divides the Eastern from the Western hemisphere along its entire length. For two thirds of its course only navigators are interested in this fact, as the line crosses enormous expanses of ocean. Many more people are interested in knowing where it crosses on land. Towns and villages straddle both hemispheres, many people live in one and work in the other, and in extreme cases houses are bisected by the Meridian. Do you sleep in the East and breakfast in the West?

(2) *The Greenwich Meridian superimposed on an artificially coloured image of the Earth from space.*

THE MERIDIAN THROUGH ENGLAND

From North to South Pole the only land the Greenwich Meridian crosses is that of Western Europe, Western Africa and Antarctica. Its path through England is from the North East coast near Withernsea to the South Coast and the English Channel at Peacehaven. The line of the Meridian has been specially drawn on these extracts from Ordnance Survey Routemaster maps which are at a scale of 1:250 000 (about 1 inch to 4 miles).

The most northerly land crossed by the Greenwich Meridian is low and open. The line misses Withernsea but goes straight through Patrington Windmill. It then crosses Sunk Island Sands and on into the River Humber estuary. On the south of the Humber is Cleethorpes and its 3 miles of sand which have made it a popular seaside resort since Victorian times. In the low lying country to the south of the town is Brackenborough Hall and the deserted medieval village of Brackenborough. Both are on the Meridian.

One of the many plaques marking the Meridian's route can be seen at Eastgate in Louth – a market town set on the eastern edge of the Lincolnshire Wolds. Its early 15th century Parish Church, well known for its 295ft tower, appears in J M W Turner's painting of the Horse Fair at Louth.

Moving south, the Meridian crosses the eastern edge of the Wolds, an area of rolling hills and secluded valleys. The Romans were active here, although it was the Danes who contributed most. The names of many villages ending in 'by' give evidence of Danish influence; Hareby on the Meridian and Lusby, Asgarby and East Kirkby very close by. Somersby, another tiny Wold village is perhaps the best known. In 1809 Alfred Lord Tennyson (3) was born here. He also went to school 'on the meridian' at Louth. He later became one of the great figures of the Victorian era and was Poet Laureate from 1850 until his death in 1892. Close by is Harrington Hall, where the gardens are said to have been the inspiration for Tennyson's famous line 'Come into the garden, Maud'.

Bolingbroke Castle, in Old Bolingbroke a mile from the Meridian, was the birthplace of Henry

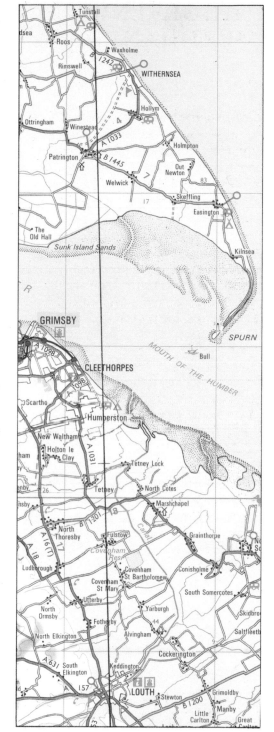

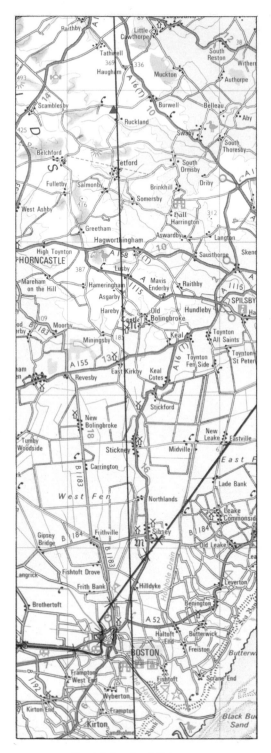

(3) *Alfred Lord Tennyson. The photograph is by Julia Margaret Cameron.*

IV. Only the remains of the castle can be seen today. Old Bolingbroke was a major market town in the Middle Ages, but no longer. However, a town that has retained its importance as a commercial centre is Boston (on the Meridian). The River Witham gave Boston access to Flanders and parts of Northern Europe and made it, 800 years ago, one of the most important commercial centres in the country. It was from here in the early 17th century that the Pilgrim Fathers set forth to seek religious freedom. They eventually settled in America where their new home (now much larger than the original) became Boston, Massachusetts.

South of Boston is the South Holland District, an area of typical fen country where there are numerous smallholdings and farms. It is well drained by a series of intersecting small canals, dykes and drains. Although the Meridian passes just to the west of Holbeach, it passes through Holbeach Clough, then Throckenholt and straight through the school in Somersham. The closest the line gets to Cambridge is Clare College Farm and the radio telescopes of the Institute of Astronomy. Then, further southward, it just clips Orwell.

Royston, on the borders of Hertfordshire and Cambridgeshire, grew up at the intersection of two ancient roads: Ermine Street which ran north–south connecting York, Lincoln and London, and the Icknield Way which ran along the chalk ridge from Salisbury and on into East Anglia. The Meridian crosses Ermine Street (now the A10) twice and runs close to it for nearly 25km (16 miles). Look out for the golf course which is in two hemispheres 1km north east of Puckeridge, and Noah's Ark – a farm

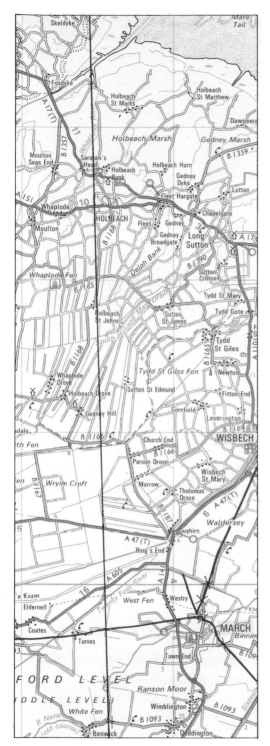

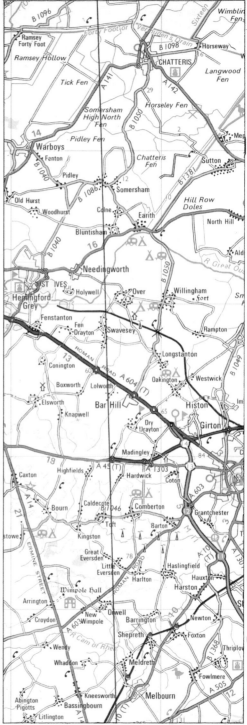

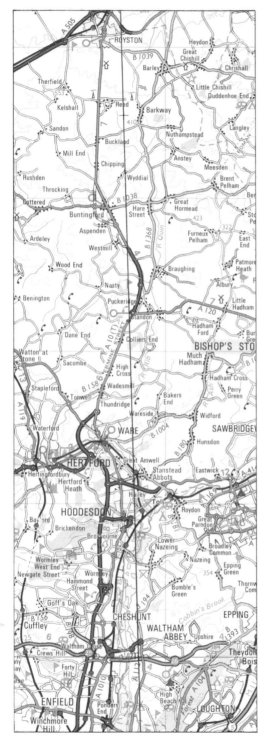

right on target. The village of Cold Christmas is just east of the Meridian.

Very close to Ware the Meridian enters the Lee (or Lea) Valley which runs almost due north–south for about 40km (25 miles) until the River Lee enters the Thames. The Meridian crosses the Lee at the north end of the valley and then runs parallel with it on the east bank. The whole of this area has been developed to cater for a range of leisure activities including a 'meridian walk'. In the valley and bisected by the Meridian is Waltham Abbey, where King Harold (killed by an arrow in his eye at the Battle of Hastings (32)) is said to be buried. The Meridian is marked in the town's rose garden. The Abbey Church (4), dating from the 11th century, has a peal of 12 bells in the 16th century tower which inspired Tennyson's poem *In Memoriam* ('ring out wild bells') – yet another Meridian connection for Tennyson. Much of *In Memoriam* was written at nearby High Beach less than half a league from the Meridian and reputed to be the haunt of the highwayman Dick Turpin.

(4) *Waltham Abbey. The tower holds one of the finest peals of bells in England.*

(5) *The Chingford Pillar, marking Bradley's meridian, is on the left. Zero longitude is marked 19ft to the east.*

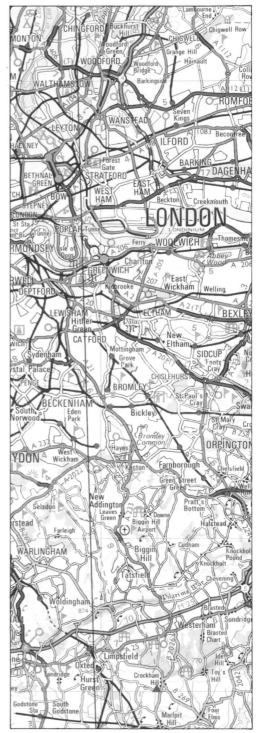

On Pole Hill at Chingford on the edge of Epping Forest is a stone pillar (5). It marks a Greenwich meridian, but not the one defined by Airy's transit circle (see FIVE *Maps and Charts*). The Chingford Pillar, erected in 1824, marks the Greenwich meridian as defined by the 8ft transit instrument of James Bradley, third Astronomer Royal. This meridian was replaced by that of Airy in 1851 when he set up his new transit instrument to the east of Bradley's. The Chingford Pillar bears the inscription ' . . . the line of zero longitude lies 19 feet to the east of this pillar'.

Moving southwards, the line enters the predominantly residential areas of Waltham Forest, Walthamstow, Leyton, Stratford and Newham, then across the Thames to Greenwich (6,7), Lewisham, Beckenham, West Wickham and New Addington. The path of the Meridian is marked on the banks of the Thames and in a number of other places throughout the Greenwich area. In the courtyard of the Old Royal Observatory at Greenwich a brass strip divides East from West *(front cover)*. This is a favourite spot for taking photographs as visitors straddle both hemispheres, or stand on tiptoe in no mans land. Not so easy to photograph, but still on the Meridian is Hither Green Station, 3km (2 miles) from the Observatory. The line is marked in the underground passage which connects the East on one side of the tracks to the West on the other.

On the edge of the Ashdown Forest is East Grinstead; this town marks the Meridian in a very special way by including its representation in the form of a white line in the town's coat of

(6) *The Old Royal Observatory, Greenwich, viewed from the north. The left of the picture is of the Eastern Hemisphere, the right of the West.*

(MAP) *This extract from an Ordnance Survey Pathfinder map at a scale of 1:25 000 (about 2 1/2 inches to 1 mile) has been highlighted to show the National Maritime Museum and Greenwich Park (green), and the Meridian (red).*

(7) *Aerial view of Greenwich Park, looking north. The Meridian passes through the Old Royal Observatory.*

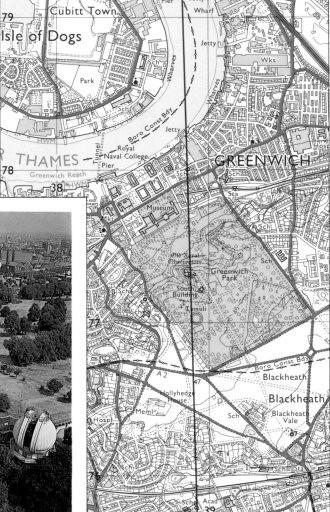

arms (8). Three kilometres (2 miles) south of East Grinstead is Weir Wood Reservoir, good for fly fishing in summer, sailing in winter and bird watching all the year round. The inn at Danehill is the only licensed Crocodile in the country. A good pint is said to rise in the yeast and set in the vest!

You can travel back to the days of steam at Sheffield Park Station, a terminus of the Bluebell Railway. Sheffield Park is a typical country station built in 1882 and is maintained in the Victorian style of the London, Brighton and South Coast Railway.

(8) *The East Grinstead coat of arms. The white line represents the Greenwich Meridian.*

(9) *This obelisk at Peacehaven marks the point where the Greenwich Meridian leaves England.*

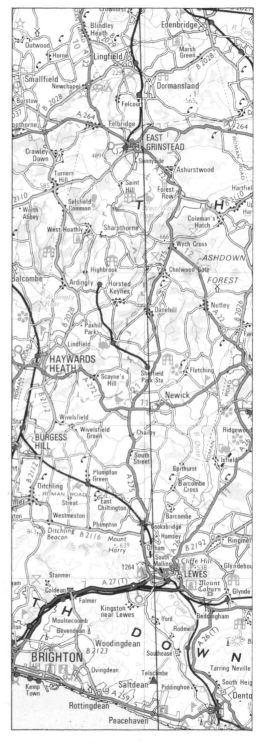

The most southerly residential areas along the line in England are Lewes, Iford and Peacehaven (once the home of Gracie Fields). Until 1914 when a businessman had the idea of a 'garden by the sea' the área where Peacehaven now stands was open country. There is an obelisk (9) with a drinking fountain at the point where the line crosses the promenade and plunges over the cliff into the sea.

FRANCE TO ANTARCTICA

Although the French have always been reluctant to accept the 'English' meridian they cannot ignore the fact that it crosses the length of their country. After leaving England and crossing the channel (via the Greenwich buoy) it arrives in France in the Baie de la Seine to the west of Le Havre. South, through Normandy (10) and Maine, missing Le Mans, it crosses the River Loire near Saumur and continues through the heart of the wine country. For the next 400km the Meridian runs parallel with the west coast of France and the Bay of Biscay passing both Cognac and Bordeaux. At the foot of the Pyrenees it passes by Lourdes and then south into Spain.

The Meridian cuts across nearly 300km of Catalonia, the north eastern area of Spain, before entering the Gulf of Valencia by Castellon de la Plana. It comes ashore again for nearly 30km on the headland opposite the island of Ibiza.

Across the Mediterranean Sea are the Atlas mountains of Northern Algeria, and then the great expanse of the Sahara Desert. For much of the 1800km stretch across the desert the

(10) *Some Normandy cows who neither know nor care how close they are to the Meridian.*

Meridian is accompanied by one of the few desert roads – the famous Route Tanezrouft to Timbuktu. The line crosses the Niger at Gao and then on to Upper Volta, Togo and Ghana where it passes through Lake Volta, the largest lake in West Africa which was created in 1964 by damming the Lower Volta River. Watch out for the crocodiles (this time unlicensed!). It leaves Africa at the Gold Coast where a rock marks the start of its long passage down through the Atlantic Ocean. Zero meets zero in the Gulf of Guinea, and then continues southwards towards Antarctica (11) – the only area of land the Meridian crosses in the Southern Hemisphere. After crossing Queen Maud Land the Meridian ends up at the South Pole.

(11) *Antarctica is the only land crossed by the Greenwich Meridian in the Southern Hemisphere.*

TWO

What are Latitude and Longitude?

If you wished to tell someone where to find you, you would probably either give your address, or specify a landmark: 'under the clock at Waterloo Station'; 'on top of Old Smokey', etc. You might even give a map reference but the recipient would still have to interpret this in terms of landmarks before he could find you. How would you manage if you were in the middle of the ocean, or in a desert where there are no landmarks? You would need to specify your latitude and longitude, so, before you venture too far from home, it is a good idea to know what latitude and longitude are, and how they may be determined.

Lines of latitude are the horizontal lines on a world map (12) which tell you how far north or south you are. Latitude is measured in degrees (°) from the equator, starting from 0° at the equator and increasing to 90°N at the North Pole or 90°S at the South Pole. Each degree can be divided into 60 minutes of arc ('). For example, the latitude of New York is 40°40'N.

Lines of longitude are the vertical lines which tell you how far east or west you are. A meridian is simply a north–south line, and longitude is measured in degrees and minutes from the meridian through Greenwich (London). Longitude starts from 0° at the Greenwich Meridian and increases to 180°E or 180°W. For example, the longitude of New York is 73°50'W of Greenwich.

For anyone who has difficulty in remembering which is which, lATitude is distance from the equATor and LONgitude is measured from LONdon. Another small point to clear up is the pronunciation of longitude. Some say long-itude, others prefer lon-jitude: take your pick, but avoid long-titude!

Why are latitude and longitude measured in degrees rather than, for example, miles; and why are there a total of 360° of longitude but only a total of 180° of latitude? The answer to the first part of the question is largely historical. The early navigators could measure their latitude fairly easily in terms of angle (it is the angle between the Pole Star and the horizon), but they could not convert this to distance, because they did not know the radius of the Earth. Also, angles are much more convenient than distances when working out navigation problems with the

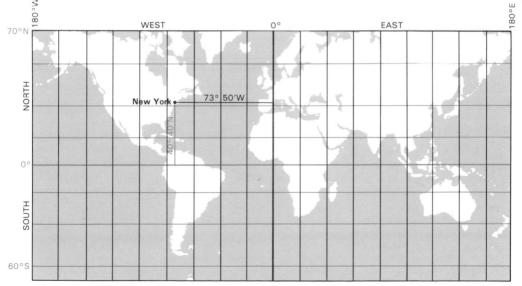

(12) *The World on Mercator's projection (see* FIVE *'Maps and Charts'), showing lines of latitude (blue) and longitude (red). New York is at latitude 40°40'N, longitude 73°50'W.*

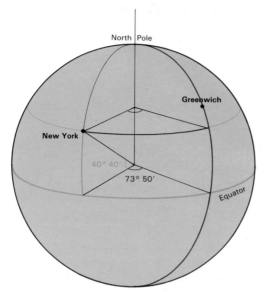

(13) *The Earth as a sphere, with latitude (blue) measured north or south of the equator, up to 90° at the poles, and longitude (red) measured east or west of the meridian through Greenwich.*

aid of globes. For reasons that will be discussed later, it might have been better to measure longitude in terms of time rather than angle. Regarding the second part of the question, latitude goes only half way round the Earth – from pole to pole – but longitude goes all the way round back to where it started (13). However, a degree of latitude is very nearly* the same length (about 111 km or 69 miles) whether it is near the equator or near the poles, whereas the length of a degree of longitude decreases from 111 km (69 miles) at the equator to 84 km (52 miles) at the latitude of New York, and right down to zero at the poles.

While on the subject of degrees and length, it is interesting to note that the metre was originally defined as one ten-millionth of the distance from the pole to the equator and that a nautical mile corresponds to one sixtieth of a degree of latitude (i.e. one minute of arc). A knot is one nautical mile per hour, so a ship sailing at 10 knots would take 6 hours to cover one degree.

Back to longitude: why is longitude measured from Greenwich? This booklet was written to

* Very nearly rather than exactly because the Earth is not a perfect sphere.

answer this question fully: the short answer is that, unlike latitude where the equator and poles provide obvious starting and finishing points, there is no natural starting point for longitude. Any meridian will do, and the choice of the Greenwich meridian is quite arbitrary.

WHY DO WE NEED TO KNOW OUR LONGITUDE?

It has already been suggested that latitude and longitude are necessary to arrange meetings in featureless parts of the World. This may not seem desperately important until you consider the nature of some of these meetings. For example, it is highly desirable to meet up with an oasis when travelling across the desert, or to meet up with a port at the end of a sea voyage. It is also useful to avoid unexpected meetings with rocky islands in the middle of the night!

Nowadays we take it for granted that a ship, plane or camel knows where it is all the time, and can unerringly find its way to its destination without bumping into obstacles on the way. This was not always the case, and there are many examples of disasters at sea that were the direct result of ignorance of position. In 1707, for example, the fleet of Vice Admiral Sir Cloudesley Shovell was wrecked on the rocks of the Scilly Islands on a dark October night, with the loss of 2000 lives; it believed it was heading safely into the English Channel (14). Another example that shows the problem to be essentially one of finding longitude is that of Anson sailing the *Centurion* round Cape Horn in 1741. The approved method was to sail first south, then west until clear of the Horn, and finally north on the other side. Anson assumed he had gone far enough west until his northward leg brought him, unexpectedly, towards land. He had to repeat the operation with serious loss of time during which his men were dying of scurvy. It was important to get them ashore as soon as possible, so he headed due north until he reached the latitude of Juan Fernandez, but he had no idea if the island was to the east or west of him. He tried west initially, but failed to find the island (in fact he was by then very close) so turned around and sailed east until he sighted not the island but the Spanish occupied coast of Chile. He would have been less than welcome there, so he had to turn yet again and eventually reached Juan Fernandez nearly two weeks after his first close approach. During this time some 70 of his men had died.

Many other examples could be cited, but these two should show that some means of finding position at sea was of vital importance and not just an academic exercise. As well as finding one's own position it was important to know the positions of the hazards to be avoided and the havens to be reached. This was a slightly easier problem since the observations needed to determine the positions of coasts and islands could be made on land, which is much easier than from the heaving deck of a ship. Nevertheless, accurate surveying and map making were every bit as important as the determination of a ship's position.

(14) *Sir Cloudesley Shovell's fleet wrecked on the Scilly Isles, 1707. Artist unknown.*

HOW DO WE FIND LATITUDE AND LONGITUDE?

In principle there is no difficulty in finding latitude and longitude, and in practice it is quite easy to find latitude. The only real problem, then, is the practical determination of longitude. How this problem was solved will be discussed later; for the present we will consider only the principles.

First latitude. The North Pole can be considered not only as a point in the Arctic, but also as a position in the heavens directly over that point. This celestial North Pole is the point about which the stars appear to rotate (actually, it is the Earth that does the rotating) and it is very close to Polaris, the Pole Star. Latitude is the angle between the equator and the vertical, and it can easily be shown that this is also the angle between the celestial North Pole and the horizon. Thus we can measure our latitude to within one degree simply by measuring the angle between Polaris and the horizon.

When Polaris is not visible, or if higher accuracy is required, any other astronomical object that is on or near the north–south line can be used, such as the Sun near midday, or the Moon, planets or stars. Again, the altitude is measured (altitude is the angular height above the horizon), but because the object is not at the North Pole, the angle has to be adjusted by adding or subtracting the North Polar Distance (NPD) of the object, before the latitude can be found. The NPD is found from navigational tables, such as the *Nautical Almanac* (see SEVEN *Tools of the Trade*). When an astronomical body is close to the meridian its altitude is nearly constant, so the exact time of observation is not critical.

The trick in measuring the difference in longitude between two places is to consider the difference not as an angle, but as time. This is best explained with the aid of an illustration (15) which shows the Earth viewed from above the North Pole. From this position, all meridians

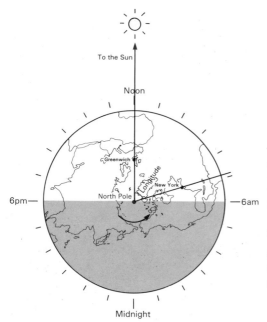

appear as radial lines. We have chosen the instant when the Sun is in line with the Greenwich Meridian, so the time at Greenwich is noon and the time at a point on the other side of the world (longitude 180°W) will be midnight. In New York the time would be about seven in the morning. As time passes, the Earth will rotate in the direction shown by the arrow, but the clock dial will remain fixed relative to the Sun. Obviously, the time at any site will not stand still, but the difference in time between two fixed sites will always be the same, and this difference is a direct measure of the longitude. We have seen that 180° of longitude corresponds to 12 hours of time, so 15° corresponds to 1 hour of time. Therefore, to convert from hours to degrees, simply multiply the number of hours by 15.

The sort of time we are talking about here is *apparent solar time*, which is the time told by a sundial, rather than *civil time* – the time on a watch. If we have a sundial that is indicating, say, 9.30am and we know by some means that at the same instant, a sundial in Greenwich indicates 11.30am then we deduce that we are *west* of Greenwich (since our time is *earlier* than that of Greenwich) by an angle corresponding to 2 hours, which is 30°. This is how longitude is measured; all we need is our own time, and the time at Greenwich. So what was the problem? The greatest problem was in finding out Greenwich time when you were remote from Greenwich. A lesser, but still difficult problem was accuracy. Remember that on the equator one degree of longitude is about 111km; this corresponds to 4 minutes of time. Thus to measure your position to an accuracy of 1km you would need to know the difference between your own time and Greenwich time to an accuracy of 2 seconds.

Clearly, time and longitude are intimately connected, so we will have a section on time before returning to the main story.

(15) *Time depends on longitude: when it's noon at Greenwich, it is 7am in New York (longitude 73°50′W) and midnight at 180° longitude. As the Earth rotates, the Sun and clock-face remain fixed and the time at Greenwich and New York moves on; however the difference between Greenwich time and New York time does not change, and this difference can be used to measure the longitude.*

THREE

Time and its Measurement

Until very recently time has been measured by reference to the movements of the Earth, Sun, Moon and stars: a year is the time it takes for the Earth to orbit the Sun; a month is the time for the Moon to orbit the Earth; and a day is the time for the Earth to rotate once about its axis. In this chapter we are concerned with the day; once this has been defined, hours, minutes and seconds follow simply by dividing by 24, then 60 then 60 again.

One of the desirable properties of a system of time measurement is that it should proceed at a uniform rate, i.e. all the seconds (or hours or days) should be of the same length. If the rotation of the Earth is to be used as our fundamental clock, it is important to know if it always takes the same time to complete a revolution about its axis. John Flamsteed, the first Astronomer Royal – of whom more later – made a careful check on the length of the day and found it to be constant within the errors of the best mechanical clocks then available: these were the year clocks by Thomas Tompion mounted in the Octagon Room of the Old Royal Observatory (16). Nearly 300 years passed before mechanical timekeepers in the form of quartz clocks achieved sufficient accuracy to show that there *are* small variations in the rate of the Earth's rotation. For present purposes these tiny departures from uniform rotation can be ignored, although they are of great importance to geophysicists for the information they give about the Earth's interior and the circulation of the atmosphere.

TIME BY THE STARS

Because of the Earth's rotation about its axis (in an anticlockwise direction when viewed from Polaris), the Sun, Moon, stars and planets all appear to rotate in the opposite direction, when viewed from Earth. You can measure the length of a day by noting the direction of one of these objects, and then timing how long it takes for

(16) *Year-clocks by Thomas Tompion were presented to John Flamsteed by Sir Jonas Moore, and mounted in the Octagon Room of the Old Royal Observatory. These clocks were used to check the uniformity of the Earth's rotation. The original clocks still exist, one in the British Museum and another in private hands. Those now in the Octagon Room (shown here) are reproductions.*

that object to get back to the same position. If the object you choose is the Sun, the interval will be a solar day, if a star is used it will give a sidereal day. When an astronomer, such as Flamsteed, wishes to measure the Earth's rotation rate, he almost invariably chooses to do so by observing the stars rather than the Sun. This is not because astronomers only come out at night, but, as we shall see in the next section, because sidereal time is much easier to work with than solar time.

Light passing through the Earth's atmosphere gets bent so that a star always appears to be slightly higher above the horizon that it actually is. This effect is greatest near the horizon, and diminishes to zero towards the point vertically overhead (the zenith). Thus, it is best to observe stars when they reach their greatest altitude in the sky, and this occurs when they cross the observer's meridian. Also, the stars appear to be moving east–west as they cross the observer's meridian, whereas the atmospheric distortion is then north–south, so the time of meridian crossing is not affected. For these reasons it is usual to measure sidereal time by noting the instant when a star crosses the observer's meridian. The time that elapses between this instant and the next occasion when the same star crosses the same meridian is a sidereal day. No matter which star is chosen, the interval will always be the same.

This defines the length of a sidereal day, but when does the day start and finish? Just as we are free to choose anywhere on the Earth from which to measure longitude, so we can choose any position amongst the stars and start our sidereal day from the time when the chosen point crosses our meridian. By convention, this position is chosen by astronomers to be the 'first point of Aries', for which they use the symbol ♈ (this will be familiar to those of you born between March 21 and April 20 as the symbol for the zodiacal sign of Aries, the ram). The first point of Aries marks the position amongst the stars where the Sun's orbit crosses from south to north i.e. it is the position the Sun occupies at the vernal equinox, which occurs on or near March 21. The significance of this will emerge in the next section *Time by the Sun*; for the present, it merely marks the celestial equivalent of zero longitude.

As its name suggests, the first point of Aries was originally located in the astronomical constellation of Aries, the ram. However, unlike earthly latitudes and longitudes, astronomical coordinates do not remain fixed but drift around very slowly due to a phenomenon called precession. Because of this, the first point of Aries is now in the constellation of Pisces, the fishes.

A sidereal day starts when the first point of Aries crosses our meridian. At the instant when this occurs we may set our sidereal clock to 0 hours. As time passes, stars will pass across our meridian, and any given star will always do so at the same sidereal time. The sidereal time of the meridian passage of a star is called its Right Ascension, or RA, and is the astronomical equivalent of longitude. (The astronomical equivalent of latitude is called Declination; a star's direction is completely specified by its RA in hours, minutes and seconds and its declination in degrees.) Once we know the RA of a star, we can use this star to determine sidereal time by setting our clock to the RA of the star as it crosses our meridian.

We now have all the information we need to determine sidereal time, but how will our time compare with that of someone in a different part of the World? We have already seen that sidereal time goes at a uniform rate, because of the uniform rate of rotation of the Earth, so the only difference will be in the starting point. The first point of Aries appears to move from east to west, so it will cross our meridian (and start our sidereal day) earlier than it will cross the meridian of someone west of us, so his time is behind ours. If he is 15 degrees of longitude to our west, the time difference will be one hour. Similarly, the sidereal time of someone 30 degrees east of us will be two hours ahead of ours. Thus, when we use sidereal time, we should always specify the geographical longitude to which it refers. Astronomers usually recognise two sorts of sidereal time: local sidereal time which refers to their own location, and Greenwich sidereal time.

Anyone who lives in the Northern Hemisphere and who knows how to find the Pole Star from the pointers of the Great Bear (or plough, or big dipper, or Ursa Major; call it what you will) can easily find their local sidereal time as follows. Visualise the Pole Star as the centre of the dial of a 24 hour clock with 11 hours at the top, and the pointers as its only hand. Just one slight catch – the hand goes anticlockwise! When the pointers are above the Pole Star, local sidereal time is 11 hours; when they are below the Pole Star it is 23 hours; when they are to the left of the Pole Star it is 17 hours, and to the right 5 hours (17).

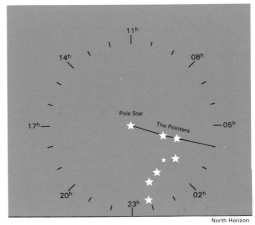

(17) *The Pointers of the Great Bear indicating 4 hours local sidereal time.*

TIME BY THE SUN

Since we regulate our lives by the Sun, getting up in the morning and going to bed at night (except, perhaps, for astronomers), it might seem more logical to determine time from the Sun rather than the stars.

Time by the Sun, known as solar time, can be determined in just the same way as sidereal time, by noting the time at which the Sun crosses our meridian. The interval between two such crossings gives us a solar day, and the time of crossing is midday. With the stars, the time of crossing of the first point of Aries marked the start of the day, but a half-day adjustment is made in the case of the Sun to avoid the inconvenience of changing the date in the middle of the working day. (For the same reason, astronomers used to measure solar days from noon to noon.) Just as for sidereal time, the solar time we determine in this way will be local solar time, and will differ by 1 hour for every 15 degrees of longitude from the time determined by people elsewhere. In the words of the hymn 'The Sun that bids us rest is waking our brethren neath the western sky'.

Apart from the 12 hour difference, why should solar time differ from sidereal time? After all, the Sun itself is a star. There *is* a difference and it results from the fact that, besides spinning on its axis, the Earth orbits the Sun once a year, and this causes the position of the Sun against the background of distant stars to change from day to day. Let us suppose that the Sun and a star cross our meridian at the same time. Twenty-four sidereal hours later, the star will be back on the meridian, but, because the Earth has moved on in its orbit, approximately 4 more minutes will pass before the Sun is back on the meridian (18). In the course of a year, the Earth makes a complete revolution around the Sun, so the difference between solar time and sidereal time is exactly one day per year. There are 366¼ sidereal days and 365¼ solar days in a year, so solar clocks tick slower than sidereal clocks in the ratio 365¼:366¼.

At the vernal equinox (on or near March 21), the Sun is in the same direction as the first point of Aries, so the start of a sidereal day corresponds to midday solar time; 6 months later, at the autumnal equinox, sidereal and solar time

To a Star

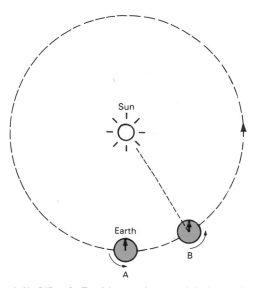

(18) *When the Earth is at* A, *the star and the Sun are in the same direction. One sidereal day later, the Earth has moved to* B; *the star is still in the same direction (or it would be if the diagram was drawn to scale, with the star very, very far away) but the Sun is about one degree wrong, so a further 4 minutes will elapse before a solar day is completed.*

are the same. If we start measuring sidereal time from the autumnal equinox and multiply it by 365¼/366¼, we get solar time. Incredible as it might seem, this is the way astronomers determine Greenwich Mean Time.

Why do they not do the obvious thing, and measure solar time directly from the Sun? The reason is that the small difference between the sidereal day and the solar day – the part that takes account of the Earth's orbital motion round the sun – varies from day to day. There are two reasons for this. The first is that the Earth's orbit is an ellipse rather than a perfect circle, and at some parts of the year the Earth is nearer to the Sun than at others. The Earth moves most rapidly in its orbit when it is closest to the Sun (in December) and rather more slowly when it is farthest away (in June). The second reason is that the Earth's rotation axis is not perpendicular to the plane of the Earth's orbit so that from April to August the Sun is north of the equator, and from October to February it is south. While the Sun is moving away from the equator, the difference between sidereal and solar day is less than it is when the Sun is moving towards the equator. These differences from the average, or mean, length of day never amount to as much as half a minute, but they build up so that a clock corrected to the meridian crossing of the Sun would be over 14 minutes fast in February and over 16 minutes slow in November compared with a clock that went at a constant, average rate – i.e. a clock telling mean time.

The time told by a clock based on the position of the Sun is called *apparent solar time*, and the amount by which this leads or lags behind mean time is called the *equation of time*. For many centuries apparent solar time, as shown by a sundial for example, was quite adequate (so long as it wasn't cloudy), but since the advent of accurate mechanical timekeeping, mean time has come into almost universal use.

To summarise:

Sidereal time is time by the stars and goes at a uniform rate. It may be measured as illustrated in (17) by using the line from Polaris to the pointers as the hand of a clock.

Mean solar time is an approximation to time by the Sun. It goes at a constant rate, slightly slower than sidereal time so that it 'loses' exactly one day per year. It may be measured with a nocturnal (19) which is essentially similar to the sidereal 'clock in the sky', but has an additional plate to allow for the adjustment of about 4 minutes per day throughout the year. The nocturnal is held at arms length with the handle vertical and the Pole Star visible through the centre hole. The long moving arm is lined up with the pointers of the Great Bear, and time is read off from the position of the arm on a clock dial, which has been rotated against a calendar dial.

Apparent solar time is based on where the Sun actually appears in the sky, but has the disadvantage of going at a non-uniform rate. It can be measured with a sundial (20).

(19) *The nocturnal is used for measuring mean solar time at night. The Pole Star is viewed through the centre hole, the handle is held vertical and the rotating arm is lined up with the Pointers of the Great Bear. Adjustment from sidereal time to mean solar time is made by rotating the hour plate to the appropriate date; about one degree for each day. This example is by John Browne, c.1660.*

(20) *The familiar sundial measures apparent solar time, which can differ from mean solar time by as much as a quarter of an hour. This example is by Elias Allen, c.1635.*

All three types of time need to be further quali-
fied to say if they are *local*, i.e. relating to the
meridian of the observer, or if they refer to some
standard meridian, such as *Greenwich*.

Before the days of high-speed travel and com-
munication, each town kept its own local time,
but nowadays it is more convenient if the same
time is kept over a very wide area. For example,
Greenwich Mean Time is adopted for the whole
of the United Kingdom (as well as Portugal and
a large chunk of Africa) although it is strictly
valid only for the meridian of Greenwich. The
world is divided into a series of zones, each
about 15° wide and roughly centred on a
meridian that is a multiple of 15° from Greenwich, each of which keeps *Zone Time* which is the
mean solar time of the central meridian (see 49).

TIME AT SEA

The additional problems associated with
determining time at sea (determining as
opposed to carrying it around on a watch, or
listening to the radio) are (i) the lack of stability:
it is no good trying to set up an accurate
north–south telescope when the deck won't
stand still, (ii) uncertainty of position, which
makes it difficult to adjust from local time to
Greenwich time, and (iii) movement through
the water, which means that a series of observations cannot be made in the same position. This
last problem is not too serious, as allowance can
easily be made for a steady movement in a
straight line, which is usually a good approximation to the movement of the ship. The lack of
stability means that you have to abandon the
idea of a telescope on a rigid mounting in favour
of a hand-held sextant, which can measure the
angle between two objects, usually the angle
between the Sun or a star and the horizontal –
the altitude. Since we have lost our north–south
line, it is no longer possible to determine local
time from a single observation. However, observations of the altitude of two separate stars will
define local time uniquely. Alternatively, two
observations of the altitude of the Sun taken at
different times will define local time, provided
due allowance is made for the time interval
between the observations.

Having found local time, we now want Greenwich time, so that we can find our longitude

from the difference between the two. The only
way we can do this is by observing some event
that we know is going to occur at a specified
Greenwich time. Nowadays, we might use the
six pips, since we know the Greenwich time at
which they are broadcast. In earlier times, people had to rely on some astronomical event that
could be accurately predicted. One possibility
was provided by the four brightest moons of the
planet Jupiter (21). These moons were discovered by Galileo, and in the course of their
orbits they disappear from view when they are
cut off from the Sun's light by Jupiter: when this
happens they appear to be switched off at the
same time for any observer anywhere on the
Earth. The only problem is that a hand-held
telescope on the deck of a ship is not quite good
enough to make such an observation.

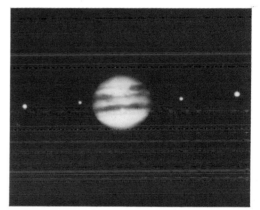

(21) *Jupiter's 4 brightest moons (Io, Europa,
Ganymede and Callisto) were discovered by Galileo.
The times of their eclipses by the planet can be used as a
universal clock.*

A more practical method is to measure the position of the Moon amongst the stars. In essence
this method uses the heavens as a clock with
the stars as a dial and the Moon as a hand (22).
Just as the Sun makes a complete circuit relative
to the stars in a year, so the Moon makes a
circuit in a lunar sidereal month of about $27^{1}/_{2}$
days. The Sun's movement corresponds to
about 4 minutes a day, whereas that of the Moon
is about 52 minutes a day. The really important
difference, though, is that the stars can be seen
at the same time as the Moon whereas the Sun
blots out everything else. This means that we
can measure the angular distance between the
Moon and a star, and then go to an almanac

which will tell us the precise Greenwich time at which the Moon and the star have that separation. As we shall see later, the preparation of such an almanac, and the development of a device for the accurate measurement of angles at sea were far from trivial problems. Also, there are further small but important corrections to be made to allow for the slightly different view of the Moon obtained from different parts of the world (parallax) and for the displacement of the images because the light from them is bent by the Earth's atmosphere (refraction). These fine adjustments cannot be ignored, as an error of only one minute of arc in the Moon's position would give an error of two minutes of time, which corresponds to an error in longitude of over 50km (30 miles). Nevertheless, it *is* possible to determine Greenwich Mean Time (GMT) at sea by the method of lunar distances, and hence find the longitude. Indeed, for many years this appeared to be the only possible method.

(22) *The 'method of lunar distances' uses the Moon as the hand of a clock and the stars as the dial. In one day, the Moon moves about 13° relative to the stars, making a complete circuit in a lunar sidereal month of 27 ¹/₂ days.*

FOUR

Towards the Solution

THE ASTRONOMER'S SOLUTION

Although astronomers put forward a number of proposals for solving the longitude problem, it was the lunar distance method, already described in detail above (THREE *Time and its Measurement*), that became their real candidate. In theory, this method of using the fairly fast movement of the Moon against the background of stars offered the best hope of finding longitude. This solution was put forward by a Frenchman known as Le Sieur de St Pierre, in the late 17th century, when he claimed he had found the answer to the longitude problem. The method was not new, but he made his claim to Louise de Kerouaille, Duchess of Portsmouth (23) and principal mistress of King Charles II. We know little of the Frenchman, but his claim and the influence of Louise were to play an important part in the longitude story.

Charles II (24) appointed a Royal Commission in December 1674 to examine Le Sieur's proposals. The seven commissioners asked John Flamsteed to assist them. He told them that Le Sieur's method was basically sound in theory, but could not be achieved in practice.

There were three large problems in their way. *Neither the positions of the stars, nor the movement of the Moon were known accurately enough for the method to work, nor was there an instrument that could measure the position of the Moon amongst the stars to the required accuracy.*

THE FOUNDING OF THE OBSERVATORY

When Charles II heard of the practical difficulties of the astronomer's solution, he determined that these should be overcome and that this work should be carried out in royal fashion. A royal warrant was issued appointing John Flamsteed as 'astronomical observer . . . to apply himself with the most exact care and dili-

(23) *Louise de Keroualle, Duchess of Portsmouth, King Charles II's favourite and friend of Le Sieur de St Pierre who claimed to have found the longitude. From an oil painting by Mignard.*

(24) *King Charles II, the founder of the Royal Observatory, Greenwich. Miniature by Samuel Cooper c.1665.*

gence to the rectifying the tables of the motions of the heavens, and the places of the fixed stars, so as to find the much-desired longitude of places, for the perfecting the art of navigation'.

Within days of the issue of this warrant a site for an observatory, where Flamsteed could carry out his work, had been chosen. Hyde park and Chelsea were both proposed as sites, but when Sir Christopher Wren (27) mentioned Greenwich this became the final choice. The Observatory was built in 1675, on the foundations of Greenwich Castle, on high ground in the centre of the Royal Park at Greenwich (25,26). The cost was kept to a minimum by using the existing foundations, and other secondhand materials.

(25) *The Royal Observatory c.1680, on the brow of the hill overlooking the River Thames, and the City of London in the far distance. The painting is attributed to Jan Griffier.*

While waiting for the building to be completed John Flamsteed lived in the Tower of London. As he was anxious to start work he used the north-east turret of the White Tower as a temporary observatory. In the middle of 1675 he moved to the Queen's House only a few hundred yards away from the site of the Greenwich Observatory. From here he could make astronomical observations and oversee the building work. In July 1676 he moved into the new Observatory and was now ready to start his work of cataloguing the heavens and so satisfying one of the requirements for the lunar distance method of finding longitude.

FLAMSTEED AND STAR MEASUREMENT

As Astronomer Royal, Flamsteed (29) received a yearly salary of £100. Out of this he had to provide his own instruments for making his observations. Although the Board of Ordnance paid an extra £26 for an assistant and undertook to keep the house in good repair, Flamsteed himself had to pay for any additional assistance he might need. It was fortunate that he had a patron, Sir Jonas Moore, Surveyor General of the Ordnance (28), who generously gave him some of the necessary instruments.

The two principal instruments Flamsteed used to make his observations were his 7ft mural arc (29) which cost him more than £120 and his 7ft sextant paid for by Sir Jonas Moore. Flamsteed used these two instruments to make almost 50 000 observations. He recorded the zenith distance of the heavenly bodies as they crossed his meridian, and found their right ascension by their sidereal time of transit. He could then find the declination of the body by taking into account his own latitude.

Most of the work was carried out in a small brick building at the bottom of the garden where the instruments were set up in two rooms now called Flamsteeds's Quadrant House and Flamsteed's Sextant House. Flamsteed House, the main building, was the home of the Astronomer Royal. Although the buildings remain, sadly, the whereabouts of Flamsteed's two important instruments are not known. As Flamsteed's personal property they were removed by his wife on his death.

The result of Flamsteed's diligent work was published in the three volumes of *Historia Coelestis*

(26) *This is one of a series of etchings showing the Royal Observatory and its instruments in its first full year of work, 1676. They are all by Francis Place based on drawings by Robert Thacker. This one shows the Observatory viewed from the north.*

(27) *Christopher Wren, architect of the Royal Observatory, was also an astronomer. For 18 years preceding the founding of the Observatory he had been Gresham Professor of Astronomy, and Savilian Professor of Astronomy at Oxford. From a mezzotint by J Smith after Sir Godfrey Kneller, 1713.*

(28) *(far right) Sir Jonas Moore, instigator and benefactor of the Royal Observatory and Surveyor General of the Ordnance.*

(29) *John Flamsteed (right) the first Astronomer Royal with his assistant Thomas Weston and the mural arc. This was painted by Sir James Thornhill on the south-east corner of the ceiling of the Painted Hall of Greenwich Hospital (now the Royal Naval College).*

Britannica in 1725 (30) and in *Atlas Coelestis* in 1729. This meant that one of the three requirements for the practice of the lunar distance method had been satisfied. The precise positions of the stars were known.

(30) *A page from Flamsteed's 'Historia Coelestis Britannica' Vol. III published in 1725 after his death.*

(32) *The Bayeux Tapestry shows a stylised version of Halley's comet at its 1066 return.*

(31) *Edmond Halley, second Astronomer Royal, best known for the comet named after him but respected by scientists for his widespread scientific work. Oil painting by Sir Godfrey Kneller c.1710.*

HALLEY AND THE MOON

It was left to Flamsteed's successor, Edmond Halley (31), to make the observations needed for accurately determining the moon's orbit. Although best remembered for the comet that bears his name (32), Halley has many other claims to fame and was nearing the end of a distinguished scientific career when he was appointed second Astronomer Royal in 1720 at the age of 64. Nevertheless, he embarked on an ambitious 18 year programme of lunar observations and lived to complete it. On his arrival he found the Observatory devoid of instruments but he received a re-equipment grant of £500. The first instrument he had made was a 5ft transit instrument but he abandoned this in favour of an 8ft iron mural quadrant which he used from 1725 until his death in 1742. With the completion of Halley's observations of the Moon the second set of accurate observations required for the lunar distance method was available.

MASKELYNE AND THE *NAUTICAL ALMANAC*

But all the hard work of Flamsteed, Halley and subsequent Astronomers Royal did not become available to the navigator to help him find his longitude at sea until towards the end of the 18th century. The accurate positions of the stars and Moon needed for determining longitude by means of the lunar distance method were finally published in 1766 in the *Nautical Almanac* for the year 1767 by Nevil Maskelyne, the fifth Astronomer Royal (33). Astronomical information for navigators has been published annually by the Royal Observatory ever since.

The final requirement of the lunar distance solution to the longitude problem – a means of accurately measuring the position of the Moon amongst the stars – had been provided earlier in the same century. John Hadley's invention, the octant (34), used one fixed and one moveable mirror to give images of two objects superimposed, enabling their angular separation to be read off from a scale. It was called an octant because the length of the scale was one eighth of a circle; when this was subsequently increased to one sixth of a circle, the name was changed to sextant.

(33) *Nevil Maskelyne. He is mainly remembered for his famous experiment in which he 'weighed' the Earth. The 'Nautical Almanac' was published for the first time in 1766, the year after he became fifth Astronomer Royal. Oil painting by John Downman 1779.*

(34) *An octant made of ebony and brass with ivory inlay by Basnett of Liverpool c.1840.*

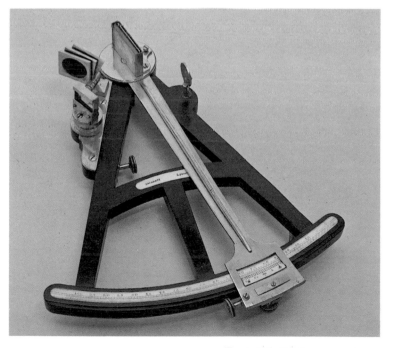

(35) *A mariner taking a lunar distance on board ship.*

With the publication of the *Nautical Almanac* the lunar distance method finally became the practical solution to the problem of finding longitude at sea (35). But it was only a short lived success as an alternative method proved to be more practical.

THE ALTERNATIVE SOLUTION

Prizes were offered by European governments in the 17th and 18th centuries to tempt someone to find a solution to the longitude problem. The rewards were magnificent; thousands of ducats from Spain, 30 000 florins from Holland and tens of thousands of pounds from England. Many were tempted, but at best won only partial grants or pensions as encouragements. Only the English prize was won outright and the winning method became the most successful answer to the longitude problem.

A prize of £10 000 was offered for finding longitude to within 1°, £15 000 to within ²/₃° and £20 000 to within ½°. A Board of Longitude was set up at the same time (1714) to administer the scheme. The £20 000 prize (worth about £1 million by today's standards) was won by John Harrison (36) who had developed a timekeeper for carrying standard time to sea. He was able to overcome the problems of designing a clock that could keep accurate time at sea; his timekeeper could cope with the motion of the vessel and changes in climate as well as keeping accurate time for months on end.

The Board was very reluctant to part with the prize money but after many years, and after producing a number of timekeepers, Harrison eventually received his prize. In the following 20–30 years, marine chronometers were produced on a commercial basis enabling all vessels to have an effective means of finding longitude. Although this method came to fruition after the lunar distance method, it was by far the more successful and long lasting.

(36) *John Harrison the outright winner of the Board of Longitude prize. Mezzotint engraving by P L Tassaert after T King showing timekeepers number 3 (H3) and 4 (H4).*

FIVE

Maps and Charts

Having found your position in terms of latitude and longitude, you need to compare it with the latitudes and longitudes of other places. Although it would be possible to do this entirely numerically with the aid of a computer, most people prefer to do it graphically, by using a chart.

The earliest navigation charts were of the Mediterranean area, drawn on goatskin or vellum and based on compass observations. These *portolani* are usually more beautiful than accurate (37), but they served their purpose for ships that never ventured too far from land. As surveying became more accurate and larger regions were mapped, a problem began to emerge: how to represent the curved surface of the Earth on a flat piece of paper? It is possible to by-pass this problem by drawing the chart on a globe, and many fine examples exist (38). While a sphere is a good approximation to the shape of the Earth, it can be made still closer by flattening it a little at the poles and allowing it to bulge a little at the equator, so that a cross section through the poles is an ellipse.

Besides giving a true representation, globes have the advantage of making it very easy to answer navigational questions, such as 'What course should I steer for the shortest route between London and New York?' However, if a globe is large enough to show any detail, it is also bulky, unwieldy and expensive. Obviously it *is* possible to represent a globe on a flat piece of paper – (38) is a flat picture of a three dimensional globe – and there are very many different ways of doing this. For example, if the camera had been closer to the globe, the region at the centre of the picture would have been enlarged relative to the regions towards the edge. These different representations are known as projections, because many of them could be obtained by using a point of light to project an image of a transparent globe onto a piece of paper. By varying the positions of the globe, light and paper, and by bending the paper into a cone or cylinder, a great variety of projections can be obtained (39).

As if this was not enough, there are yet more 'projections' which cannot actually be produced by projection, but are constructed mathematically. The best known of these is Mercator's projection (although many people believe that the credit for it should go to Edward Wright of London rather than to Gerhard Mercator of Flanders). This projection is particularly favoured by navigators because, besides having vertical lines for longitude and horizontal lines

(37) *A chart of the Mediterranean hand painted on vellum by Vesconte Maggiollo of Genoa in 1548.*

for latitude, it has the valuable property that bearings on the chart correspond to the true bearings. For example, if the line on the chart joining your present position to your destination is at an angle of 38° east of north, then that is the direction you must steer. Curiously, this is not generally the shortest route.

On Mercator's projection, lines of longitude are represented by uniformly spaced parallel lines; lines of latitude are at right angles to these, also straight and parallel, but not uniformly spaced. The scale is correct at the equator, but as you move away, either north or south, it gets more and more stretched.

The choice of projection depends on the size and shape of the area to be mapped, and the purpose for which the maps will be used. For mapping the British Isles, the Ordnance Survey chose Mercator's projection, but, to avoid excessive north–south distortion in a region which is naturally long and narrow, they turned the projection sideways into what is called the Transverse Mercator Projection. It is now the lines of latitude that are uniformly spaced, and longitude that is distorted the more you move to the east or west of the centre of the map. The centre line, corresponding to the equator in the usual Mercator projection, is chosen to be 2° west of Greenwich and along that line there is no distortion.

Having decided on the projection, it is a relatively simple matter to calculate and draw the lines of latitude and longitude as a grid on a piece of paper.

The next requirement is to plot geographical information on the paper in the correct position relative to the grid. Unfortunately latitude and longitude are not physical marks on the ground produced by a playing field white lining machine. Observations of stars and other celestial bodies are made from the ground and from these observations the latitude and longitude of the observer's position can be determined. Allowance has to be made for the fact that the Earth is not quite a uniform sphere, and then the position can be plotted on the map.

(38) *A 46cm diameter terrestial globe by Valk of Amsterdam, c.1750.*

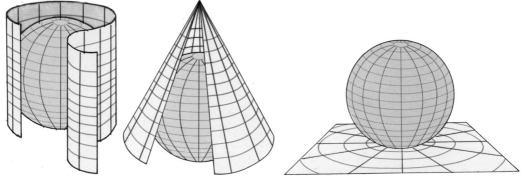

(39) *Examples of projecting latitude and longitude from the three dimensional Earth onto a two dimensional surface.*

In this way a detailed map can be built up, from which the latitude and longitude of any object can be read off. Just one further ingredient is needed before the information is complete: the scale of the map. This enables us to relate a distance on the map to a distance on the land, and involves measurements of length rather than just angles. How this is done will be explained below.

FINDING LONGITUDE BY TRIANGULATION

So far, we have considered longitude as an angle measured east or west of Greenwich, but it could equally well have been measured east or west of Paris or Rio de Janeiro, or the Great Pyramid or even 10 Downing Street (all but one of these has been seriously suggested at one time or another). Greenwich was the obvious choice for the British, since all the astronomical data in the *Nautical Almanac* were based on this site, and thus it was longitude east or west of Greenwich that was obtained from them. For the same reason it was equally logical that British charts should be drawn with the zero of longitude through Greenwich. The French did not see things the same way, though, and chose to base their longitudes on the meridian through the Paris Observatory (40). Similarly the Italians chose Naples, the Russians Pulkova, etc, so that just over 100 years ago there were more than a dozen different meridians in use.

The solution to this problem will be discussed later, but the point we wish to make here is that there is no obvious or unique starting point for measuring longitude. The only absolute measurement we can make is the difference in longitude between two places; all other longitude measurements are relative to some starting point, such as Greenwich or Downing Street. One of the more important longitude differences to measure was that between the observatories of Greenwich and Paris, so that the astronomical observations could be related for the benefit of astronomers and geographers. It was of particular importance to mapmakers for the distance to be measured in length units (metres or feet) as well as by angle. Major General William Roy undertook the English part of this joint project in 1784 by measuring a series of triangles from a base line on Hounslow Heath (now lying mostly under Heathrow Airport) through Greenwich to Dover and the French Coast (41). The French, under the supervision of Cassini de Thury, had already measured a series of triangles from Paris to the French Coast.

Why triangles? In 1784 the measurement of length was extremely difficult: the Hounslow Heath base line, 27 404.01 feet (about 8 354m) long was measured using a chain, deal rods and finally glass rods, and the work took months to complete. The measurement of angles using an instrument known as a theodolite, although still laborious, was quicker. A special theodolite

(40) *The Paris Observatory through which passes Cassini's meridian line.*

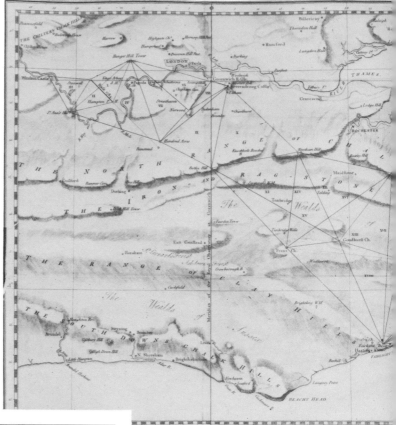

(41) *A contemporary map showing the triangulation scheme connecting the Greenwich and Paris meridians.*

(42) *Ramsden's theodolite. The sighting telescope on the top and the horizontal circle graduated in degrees, minutes and seconds are clearly discernible.*

measuring 3ft in diameter (42) was made for use in the Greenwich–Paris connection by an instrument maker called Jesse Ramsden. Using the Hounslow Heath base line as a known distance and by measuring the angles from either end of the base to a survey station (normally positioned on a high point such as a church tower) the remaining distances and angles could easily be calculated. These new distances could similarly be used as base lines for further triangles – the sides of these triangles varied from 26 000ft (about 8km) to 193 000ft (about 60km) in length (41).

Once the triangulation was complete the difference in longitude between Paris and Greenwich could be calculated by using spherical trigonometry, a knowledge of the size of the Earth and the latitudes of Greenwich and Paris. The value obtained by Roy was 2°19′42″.

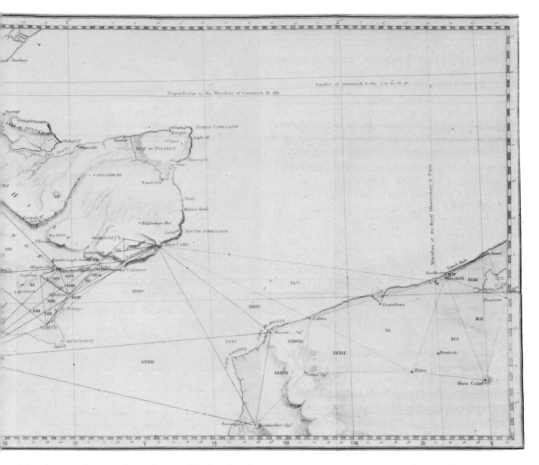

The observations made at Greenwich involved building a 30ft (12m) high scaffold on which the Great Ramsden Theodolite was placed, centred above the Bradley transit instrument which then defined the Greenwich Meridian. (James Bradley was the third Astronomer Royal.) In 1850 Sir George Airy, the seventh Astronomer Royal, had a new transit circle built, which was placed in an adjoining room to Bradley's instrument. When the Washington Conference met in 1884, it was the Greenwich Meridian defined by Airy's transit circle that was chosen as the prime meridian. As the Ordnance Survey was created in 1791 and maps had been produced based on Roy's work, the zero meridian on those maps was that defined by Bradley's meridian. Even today, after several triangulations have taken place, Ordnance Survey maps are still based on Bradley's meridian which is 0.417 seconds of arc west of the true Greenwich Meridian. The effect of this is to make the zero shown on these Ordnance Survey maps 5.9m (just over 19ft) west of the Greenwich Meridian on the South Coast and similarly 5.5m (18ft) west where it crosses the East Coast. The difference is due to the convergence of meridians of longitude towards the poles.

It was electricity, or galvanism as it was known in the 19th century, that spread Greenwich time across the country. The distribution system made use of electric clocks and the electric telegraph. An electric clock was installed at the Royal Observatory in 1852. This drove clocks in the Observatory, including a public clock by the gate (48), and provided an impulse to drop the timeball. Electrical impulses were also provided every hour for time signals along telegraph lines from the Observatory to Lewisham Station and from there along the normal railway telegraph lines to London Bridge Station. From this station the signal travelled to other stations, to the Central Telegraph Station of the Electric Telegraph Company (ETC) for distribution to post offices, public clocks and timeballs, private subscribers and via submarine cable to the continent. It was even supplied to the Royal Household at Sandringham.

(45) The timeball on the roof of Flamsteed House is easily seen from the surrounding area. The City of London is in the far distance.

(46) (right) The timeball is now electrically operated, but originally it was cranked up by hand and released by an astronomer in the basement when the clock reached 1pm.

The confusion resulting from the use of local time was much worse in other countries, especially in North America where East and West coast local times are approximately $3\frac{1}{2}$ hours different. The railways of both the USA and Canada adopted a time zone system based on the Greenwich Meridian. As had been the case in Great Britain, a system first used on the railways was very readily adopted by the community for all civil purposes.

(47) *Miss Ruth Belville 'the Greenwich time lady' setting her pocket chronometer to GMT.*

(48) *The gate clock outside the courtyard gates of the Old Royal Observatory, Greenwich. It shows Greenwich Mean Time throughout the year. The time is 9.27.*

WASHINGTON CONFERENCE 1884

By 1883 Great Britain and the North American continent were, therefore, using a common zero for their longitude and time reckoning. These two, like other countries, were realising the advantage of having a common zero for the whole World. As there is no natural zero longitude (unlike for latitude where the equator is the natural zero) countries were adopting one arbitrarily. As well as the Greenwich Meridian, Paris, Cadiz, Naples, Pulkova, Stockholm and many more were used as zero longitude by different countries. But, as Greenwich was used the most it was not surprising that this was chosen by an international conference to be the zero meridian for the World. Delegates from 25 countries met in Washington during October 1884 to discuss and possibly fix upon a meridian to be zero for longitude and time reckoning throughout the whole World.

The desirability of using one meridian was adopted unanimously, the next question was, which one? The American delegates proposed that this meridian should be that 'passing through the centre of the transit instrument at the Observatory of Greenwich'. The French were not happy about this and suggested the meridian should be neutral. After much discussion it was shown that the meridian could not be neutral, it had to pass through a scientific observatory. Furthermore, if a neutral meridian was chosen everyone would have to adopt the new system whereas if one of the systems already in use was adopted it would mean change for a smaller number of people. Greenwich was shown to be used by 65 percent of all the ships in the World and the remaining 35 percent used over ten different meridians. In the end the Greenwich Meridian was adopted, with 22 countries in favour, San Domingo against, and France and Brazil abstaining.

THE AFTERMATH

After 1884, one by one the countries not originally using the Greenwich Meridian started to use it as their longitude zero. But more noticeable, for the population at large, was the adoption of a time zone system based on this Meridian. Countries quick to adopt this included Japan, Italy, Germany, Australia and

(49) *The World's time zones, 1984.*

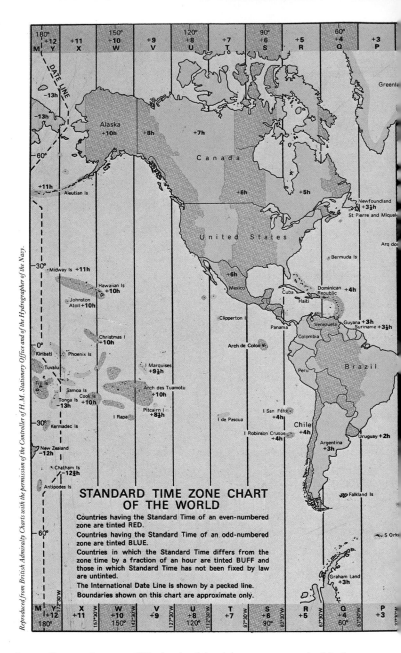

STANDARD TIME ZONE CHART OF THE WORLD

Countries having the Standard Time of an even-numbered zone are tinted RED.

Countries having the Standard Time of an odd-numbered zone are tinted BLUE.

Countries in which the Standard Time differs from the zone time by a fraction of an hour are tinted BUFF and those in which Standard Time has not been fixed by law are untinted.

The International Date Line is shown by a pecked line.

Boundaries shown on this chart are approximate only.

New Zealand. Other were slower; Portugal waited until 1912, Ireland 1916, Russia 1924, and more recently Liberia in 1972, as well as many other countries in the interim years. Until 1978 France kept 'Paris Mean Time, retarded by 9 minutes, 21 seconds', which happens to be within one fifth of a second of GMT!

The basis of the time zone system (49) is that countries using it are whole hours different from Greenwich Mean Time (except in a few instances where there is an extra half hour). So wherever you are, a time signal that announces the hour will be sufficient to correct your clock. The six-pip time signal, broadcast in the United

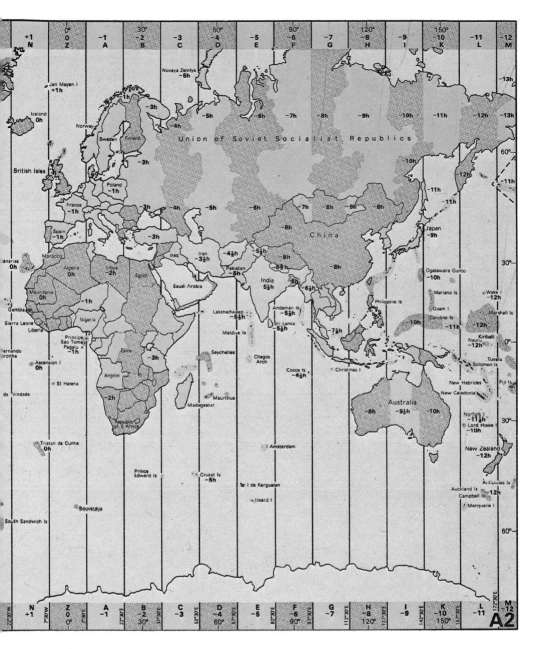

Kingdom from 1924 February 5 onwards, is such a signal. The start of the long sixth pip indicates the hour. If you cannot wait to check the time by the signal on the radio, another alternative is to telephone TIM the speaking clock. This service was brought into use on 1936 July 24 and gives the time every ten seconds.

The Greenwich Meridian is now used universally for timekeeping and navigation on land, at sea, and in the air.

SEVEN

Tools of the Trade

To a large extent the story of the Meridian and the finding of longitude is about optical and mechanical instruments. The lunar distance method was practical only after the development of mural arcs and transit circles for surveying star positions and the octant and sextant for measuring astronomical angles at sea. The final solution to the longitude problem was provided by a marine chronometer. Even the prime meridian itself is defined in terms of Airy's transit circle.

Here we look at some of these instruments in a little more detail, to see what was so special about the early ones, how they were improved, and what replaced them. One of the requirements for a navigator or astronomer has always been the *Nautical Almanac*, alias the *Astronomical Ephemeris*, or *Astronomical Almanac*. Although this is a book rather than an instrument it is, nevertheless, an essential 'tool of the trade' and will be included here.

AIRY'S TRANSIT CIRCLE

This is the instrument (51,52,53) that defines the prime meridian and has the privilege of separating East from West. It is impossible to observe through it without being in both hemispheres at once. What does it do and how does it work?

It is a specialised telescope for the fundamental measurement of star positions and time. 'Fundamental' because it does its job without need to refer to any other instrument except a clock that runs at a reasonably steady rate. You could be dropped on a desert island with nothing but the Airy transit circle, and still run a first-class time service and produce first-class star catalogues.

How it is used was described in THREE *Time and its Measurement*: star positions are measured by noting the angle the star makes with the zenith

(Zenith Distance, ZD), and the sidereal time at which they cross the meridian (their Right Ascension, RA). The actual crossing of the meridian, or transit, is observed through a telescope fitted with an accurately graduated vertical circle, and mounted to turn about an east–west axis, so that it always points to the meridian. The star catalogue is formed by listing the RA and declination of each star after making a sufficient number of observations to average out the irregularities of the clock. The declination is obtained simply by adding the zenith distance to the latitude, or subtracting it if the star transits south of the zenith. Once the catalogue has been prepared – and this takes many years – the process can be reversed. The time of transit of a star, together with its RA from the catalogue, will give a direct measure of sidereal time and can be used to correct the clock.

That is what should happen, but there are a number of things that can go wrong, and the beauty of the design of this transit circle is that Airy has incorporated the means to measure and eliminate these potential errors (50).

The first is *collimation error* (50A). This will occur if the optical axis of the telescope is not exactly at right angles to the east–west rotation axis, and will result in the transits being observed systematically to the east (or west) of the meridian. To overcome this problem, the transit circle is equipped with gear for raising the main telescope, and two supplementary horizontal telescopes, or collimators, one north and one south of the instrument, looking towards one another. With the main telescope raised, the collimators are optically aligned with one another. The main telescope is lowered onto its trunnions, and pointed first at the north collimator then at the south, and any misalignment, which can be removed by adjusting the crosswires at the eye end of the telescope, is the collimation error.

Second, it is essential that the rotation axis should be horizontal. If one end is higher than the other, the transit circle has *level error* (50B), and transits will be observed systematically to the east (or west) of the meridian, by an amount that is a maximum at the zenith and diminishes to zero towards the horizon. Level error can be measured by pointing the telescope vertically

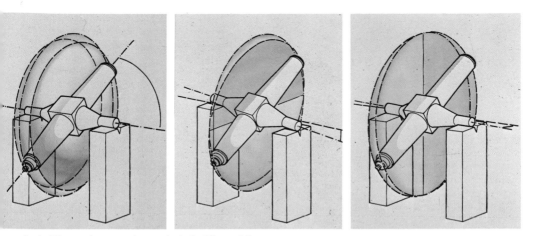

(50) *The 3 main errors of a transit circle. The meridian is shown in blue and the path followed by the telescope is shown in red.*
A *(left) Collimation error. The optical axis of the telescope may not be at right angles to the rotation axis. In this case, the line of sight is always to one side of the meridian.*
B *(centre) Level error. The axis of rotation may not be horizontal. This will give a maximum error when the telescope is vertical, zero when it is horizontal.*
C *(right) Azimuth error. The axis of rotation may not be exactly east-west. This will give a maximum error when the telescope is horizontal, zero when it is vertical.*

downwards towards a dish of mercury, which has the valuable properties of being flat, horizontal and reflective. The observer looks down the telescope and sees the crosswires and also their image reflected in the mercury. If the image coincides with the real wires, all is well. If they do not coincide, the difference in position represents twice the level error, and this can be measured and corrected for.

The last major requirement is that the rotation axis should be east–west. If not, the instrument has *azimuth error* (50C) and stars will be observed on one side of the meridian to the north, and on the other side to the south. This can be detected only by making astronomical observations, and the best stars for this purpose are those close enough to the pole to describe a complete circle around it without going below the horizon. Such a star will cross the meridian above the pole, going from east to west, and exactly 12 sidereal hours later, it will cross the meridian below the pole going from west to east. If the observed

interval differs from 12 hours the telescope has azimuth error, and the amount of the error can be deduced from the size of the difference.

These are the three main errors of a transit circle, all of which can be deduced and corrected for in the Airy transit circle. In addition, there may be some errors introduced by distortion of the frame at positions intermediate between the vertical and horizontal. It is Airy's novel attempt to eliminate some of these errors that gives his transit circle its characteristic appearance. The idea is to observe stars, not only by looking up in the usual way, but also (though obviously not on the same occasion) by looking down and seeing the image reflected in a trough of mercury. The mercury trough is situated in the observing pit, mounted on a pantograph so that it can be swung to the appropriate position for any required star while still remaining horizontal to avoid spilling the mercury. The two prominent elliptical weights on arms that extend above the telescope (51) are counterweights for the mercury trough, and the steps that surround the telescope (52) are there so that the observer can reach the eyepiece (53) for the downward observations.

To increase the accuracy of the angular measurements, the zenith-distance scale is particularly large, and to reduce the effects of nonuniform divisions it is read at six places well spaced around its circumference for each observation. It is read through 7 microscopes from the outside of the west pier, one microscope gives the degrees and the remaining 6, fitted with micrometers, give the fractions of a degree.

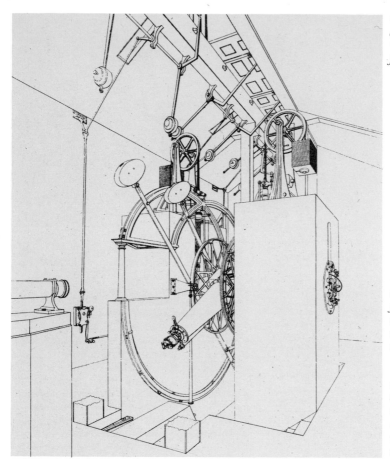

(51) *The Airy transit circle as shown in the 'Greenwich Observations' for the year 1852.*

(52) *(right) The eye end of the Airy transit circle from which electrical contacts signal the instant of transit for comparison with the standard clock.*

(53) *(far right) The steps round the Airy transit circle enable the observer to reach the eyepiece for downward observations with the image reflected by a dish of mercury.*

The timing of the transit is made by pressing a button at the appropriate moment. This sends an electrical pulse to a pen writing on paper on a rotating drum, causing it to make a tick. The time of the tick is found by comparing its position with that of similar ticks made by one–second impulses from the standard clock.

It is important to avoid wear on the trunnions on which the telescope rotates. For this reason most of the weight of the telescope is supported by counterweights acting over pulley wheels at the top of each pier. The trunnions support only ten percent of the weight, and are thus able to define the position of the telescope with minimum wear.

Airy's telescope, built in 1850 and brought into operation in 1851, was easily the most refined transit circle of the day, and differs remarkably

little from modern transit circles. The most important difference is that most later transit circles are reversible; that is, they may be removed from their mountings and replaced with the east end of the rotation axis on the west pier and vice versa. Such reversal permits the removal of further small but systematic errors. Also, the reflected transit observation was not a great success, and was discontinued both on the Airy transit circle and for subsequent transit circles.

Even today Airy's transit circle is still a first class instrument which could be used for the measurement of star positions and time. In fact, it was last used in earnest in 1954 after more than 100 years of service and over half a million observations. It has recently been refurbished and is frequently demonstrated to visitors.

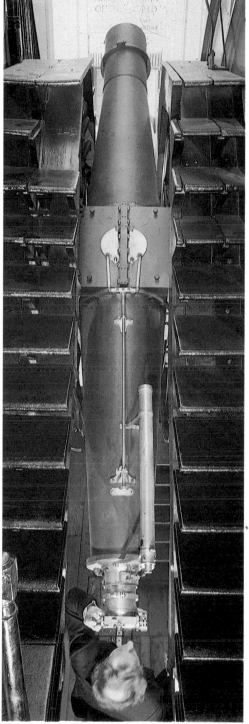

THE SEXTANT

We have already mentioned the octant, so called because its scale was one-eighth of a circle, though the mirror doubled this up so that it could measure angles of up to a quarter circle, or 90° (see 34). This was a bit restricting, and a simple increase in the length of the scale from one eighth to one sixth of a circle changed the name to sextant, and permitted the measurement of angles up to 120° (55).

The great advantage of the octant over previous instruments for measuring angles at sea, such as the mariner's astrolabe, cross-staff and back-staff, is that the two objects whose separation is being measured are both seen at the same time and in the same direction. This is all done by mirrors, one fixed and one moving (54). The observer looks directly at one object (usually the horizon) and adjusts the moving mirror until the image of the second object (a star or one edge of the Sun or Moon) is superimposed. He then notes the time and reads the angle from the scale. This was the instrument devised by John Hadley in 1730.

The present day sextant is still recognisably the same instrument, but several significant improvements (besides the lengthening of the scale) have been added over the years. The first improvement came very quickly, from Hadley himself. This was the provision of an artificial horizon – essentially a spirit level – so that altitude could still be measured, even if there was no clear horizon.

The most important improvement is the least obvious, and that is the quality of the divisions on the scale. When Hadley first invented the octant, the best instrument makers of the day, such as John Bird and George Graham, were still dividing the circle by geometrical construction using ruler and compasses. Most schoolchildren can construct 90°, 60° and 30°, though it takes some skill to do it accurately, but how do you get down to one degree, and then sixty minutes? The method used was to construct 30°, then bisect this successively to obtain 2, 4, 8, 16 ... parts. Degrees and minutes were then interpolated from these divisions with the aid of a conversion table. Despite the skill of the instrument makers, inevitably errors accumulated with the successive bisections. This process would obviously be very slow and laborious.

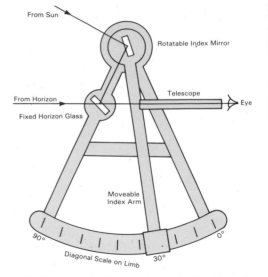

(54) *The principle of the octant. By adjusting the angle of the moveable arm carrying a mirror, a star image can be made to coincide with the image of the horizon. The angle of elevation is then read from the scale.*

(55) *(right) Sextant by Nairne and Blunt, London c.1775.*

The breakthrough in circle-dividing came in 1771 with the introduction by Jesse Ramsden of the dividing engine – a table rotated by a worm-wheel so designed that six turns of the worm correspond exactly to one degree. Using this dividing engine, not only could scales be scribed with great precision, but also very quickly and hence cheaply. A complete sextant scale could be scribed in about 45 minutes by a relatively unskilled worker.

Vernier scales were fitted to the moving arm so that the angle could be read to the precision that the accurately divided scales justified, and a telescope replaced the sighting hole, to produce the instrument as we now know it.

THE MARINE CHRONOMETER

If there is one man more than any other who deserves credit for solving the problem of finding longitude at sea, it is John Harrison who achieved what even Newton had considered impossible – the construction of a clock that would keep accurate time at sea.

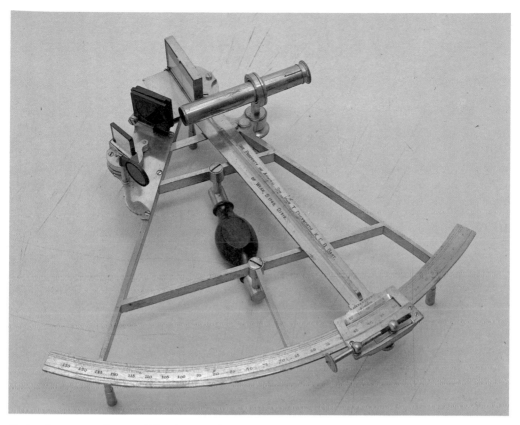

On land, accurate time could be obtained from a weight-driven pendulum clock, kept in a room at reasonably constant temperature. At sea, even in calm conditions, a pendulum would not work, and in rough conditions the weight would be more likely to smash the clock than drive it. Nor does a wooden sailing ship provide a stable temperature, particularly when sailing between the Arctic and the Tropics. Although Harrison's first marine chronometer, completed in 1735 and now known as H1 (56), looks nothing like our present ideas of such a clock, nevertheless, it overcame all these problems and performed very well when taken to sea. The pendulum was replaced with a pair of dumb-bells, pivoted at their centres, and oscillating symetrically, so that their rate of vibration would not be affected by motion of the ship. A spring replaced the weight, but with the addition of a fusee – an ingenious device to equalise the force applied to the movement regardless of whether the spring was fully wound or nearly unwound. The temperature variation was allowed for with

three brass-and-steel gridirons – an invention of Harrison which he had already applied successfully to pendulum clocks. Tests at sea in the *Centurion* in 1736 showed that the performance of H1 was sufficiently impressive to persuade the Board of Longitude to give financial encouragement to Harrison's work. Indeed, had H1 still been on board the *Centurion* six years later, it would probably have saved the lives of some 70 men by allowing Captain Anson to sail direct to Juan Fernandez (see TWO *What are Latitude and Longitude?*).

Harrison spent the rest of his life designing and building more refined marine chronometers, and eventually won the Board of Longitude prize with his fourth attempt, H4, in 1772 at the age of 79. This incorporates most of the principles of H1, although the oscillating dumb-bells are replaced with a balance wheel and the gridiron is simplified to a single bi-metallic strip. In addition H4 incorporates a remontoire, first introduced in H2, which is a small additional spring inserted between the gear train and the balance wheel, rewound at frequent intervals, so that the balance wheel is not subjected to changing forces as the main spring runs down. This was a case of 'belt and braces', as the fusee also performed this task, and subsequent chronometer makers omitted the complex remontoire with no impairment to the timekeeping. The most obvious difference between H1 and H4 is the size: H1 is a 32kg (72lb) monster whereas H4 is merely an overgrown 12cm diameter) pocket watch, albeit a very refined one (57).

Although H4 was well able to provide time to the accuracy required for finding longitude it could only be in one ship at a time. The problem of finding longitude remained until chronometers became cheap enough and plentiful enough to be carried by every ship. The first steps in this direction were taken by Larcum Kendall who, at the request of the Admiralty, first made a faithful copy of H4 to show that it could be successfully reproduced – this is known as K1 (57). Then he made a simplified version, K2, which also performed quite well enough. Both K1 and K2 achieved fame in their own right, K1 as Captain Cook's 'trusty friend, the watch' and K2 on the *Bounty* at the time of the mutiny.

(56) *John Harrison's first marine timekeeper,* H1.

(57) *Harrison's prize-winning chronometer,* H4 *(left) with the copy made by Kendall,* K1 *(right). The only obvious external difference is the two screws through the dial of* K1 *which are absent from* H4.

(58) *The traditional marine chronometer. A 2-day chronometer by Charles Frodsham of London, c.1850.*

Many clockmakers contributed to the further evolution of the chronometer. The main changes were to incorporate the temperature compensation into the balance wheel, by making it of brass and steel, and the introduction of the detent escapement, which allows the balance wheel to swing freely except for the instant it receives the impulse that keeps it going. The final version of the chronometer was not unlike H4 in size and appearance, though made of brass rather than silver, and mounted on gimbals in a wooden box (58). As with the sextant, the most important change was in the method of manufacture rather than in actual design; Harrison had produced a single masterpiece, but what was now wanted was a high quality but mass produced and reasonably priced item. A group of clockmakers in Clerkenwell, while retaining their identity and separate workshops, each specialised in the bulk manufacture of just a few parts that could be assembled by specialists. Similar 'collectives' operated elsewhere, and at last chronometers were widely and relatively cheaply available. There was still a lot of scope for individual skills, however, and some makers were significantly better than others, as was shown by their performance in the trials held at the Royal Observatory, Greenwich. These trials carried great prestige and, potentially, financial reward in the form of orders from the Admiralty. The Admiralty chronometers are still rated, cleaned and repaired at the Royal Greenwich Observatory, Herstmonceux, though the workshop is now directly responsible to the Hydrographic Department, Ministry of Defence (Navy).

The marine chronometer represents the summit of the clockmaker's art, and they are now widely collected as supreme examples of craftmanship, even though they have been superseded by quartz clocks for accuracy of timekeeping.

MARCH 1767. [35]												
Days	Stars Names	Noon.			3 Hours.			6 Hours.			9 Hours.		
		°	′	″	°	′	″	°	′	″	°	′	″
3		40	56	54	42	37	12	44	17	4	45	56	30
4		54	7	14	55	44	3	57	20	26	58	56	22
5		66	49	20	68	22	37	69	55	29	71	27	56
6	The Sun.	79	3	57	80	33	57	82	3	35	83	32	50
7		90	53	41	92	20	51	93	47	43	95	14	15
8		102	22	23	103	47	25	105	12	3	106	36	26
9		113	34	50	114	57	58	116	20	56	117	43	44
7	α Arietis.	43	16	5	44	50	10	46	24	0	47	57	33
8		25	9	1	26	33	51	27	59	4	29	24	39
9	Aldeba-	36	36	33	38	3	27	39	30	25	40	57	28
10	ran.	48	12	58	49	40	6	51	7	13	52	34	21
11		59	49	55	61	17	2	62	44	9	64	11	16

(59) *Page from the first 'Nautical Almanac' showing the predicted angular distances from the Moon to the Sun and two stars at 3-hour intervals during March, 1767.*

THE *NAUTICAL ALMANAC*

No matter how carefully a navigator makes his observations (of the position of the Moon amongst the stars for example) he will be no nearer finding his longitude until he has combined these observations with data relating to the predicted positions of the Sun, Moon and stars for that day. This is where the *Nautical Almanac* comes in, by providing these data.

When Nevil Maskelyne published the first *Nautical Almanac* in 1766, predicting the positions of the Sun, Moon and stars for 1767, he made the longitude available to any ship that carried a copy (59). Of course, the ship would also need a navigator with a means of measuring angles and a knowledge of the method of lunar distances. The latter was the main problem, as the calculations involved are far from simple and, without the aid of anything more sophisticated than tables of logarithms, it was very easy to make a mistake. Nevertheless, the elusive prize of longitude was at last available. It is little wonder that Maskelyne was not unduly impressed with Harrison's chron•meter, which must have seemed a far less realistic alternative.

Although it makes even more turgid reading than a telephone directory, the *Nautical Almanac* was an immediate success, and has been published annually ever since. It also has its imitators: the French equivalent, *Connaisance des Temps*, was quickly on the scene, but as there were no resources to compute the data, they had to use the tabulations from the *Nautical Almanac*, with the unfortunate consequences (for them) that the resulting longitudes were measured from Greenwich. Thus they had to introduce one further stage into the calculation: the addition of 2°20.2' to 'correct' the answer to the meridian of Paris.

John Pond, the Astronomer Royal after Maskelyne, was a good scientist but a poor administrator. Under his supervision, the preparation of the *Nautical Almanac* was falling behind, and it was in danger of failing to appear. Because of its importance to navigators, the Board of Visitors to the Royal Observatory set up a separate Nautical Almanac Office for its preparation, independent of the Astronomer Royal. The Nautical Almanac Office still retains its separate identity, though it is once again physically reunited with the Royal Greenwich Observatory at Herstmonceux.

In the early days the *Nautical Almanac* was primarily concerned with the data required for the lunar distance method of determining longitude. There are, however, additional astronomical data required by navigators for the determination of latitude and local time. These continued to be required after the lunar distance method was superseded.

Today, the *Astronomical Almanac*, which is the direct successor to the *Nautical Almanac*, is prepared and published jointly by the Nautical Almanac Office of the Royal Greenwich Observatory and by the US Naval Observatory. It is indispensible for all observational astronomers, and contains detailed tables of the motions of the Sun, Moon and planets, as well as information on the stars, satellites and observatories. The less detailed data required by specialist navigators and surveyors are published separately.

MODERN METHODS OF DETERMINING TIME

With the improvement of clocks, particularly when the quartz clock was introduced, it became clear that the rate of rotation of the Earth was not sufficiently uniform to remain the ultimate standard of time. Ephemeris time (used by astronomers for predicting the position of heavenly bodies) was introduced – this starts from the beginning of January 1900, and proceeds at a strictly uniform rate based on the ephemeris second, which is the appropriate fraction of the year 1900. Defining it is one thing, but obtaining it is quite another. Surprisingly, one of the best methods of determining the starting point and length of the long-departed year 1900 is a modern version of our old friend, the method of lunar distances. This involves taking a photograph of the Moon amongst the stars for subsequent precision measurement. The problem is that the stars required a longer exposure (of about 20 seconds) than the Moon, and during this time the Moon will have moved slightly relative to the stars and will give a fuzzy image. To overcome this problem, William Markowitz of the US Naval Observatory devised a special camera (60) to fit on the end of a telescope. The image of the Moon is held stationary and reduced in brightness by a disc of darkened glass which rotates through a small angle to counteract the Moon's action during the exposure.

With the still greater precision of the atomic clock (61), there is no longer any need to use stars for the measurement of time. International Atomic Time is based on the average rates of a number of sets of atomic clocks around the world, including a set at the Royal Greenwich Observatory at Herstmonceux (62). Measurements of time by the stars are still made, but this is mainly to monitor changes in the rate of the rotation of the Earth. The instrument now used is the Photographic Zenith Tube (PZT) which, as the name suggests, takes photographs of the stars as they pass vertically overhead.

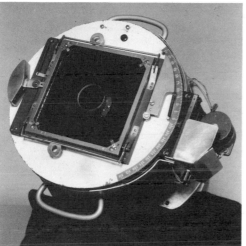

(60) *(above) The Markowitz dual-rate Moon camera – a modern version of the method of lunar distances for the determination of time.*

(61) *(above right) One box of electronics looks much like another, but this one contains an atomic clock, accurate to better than 1 second in 4000 years.*

(62) *The Time Department of the Royal Greenwich Observatory, Herstmonceux. Here, time from a set of atomic clocks is compared with time from other institutions around the World, it is supplied to users including British Telecom (for the speaking clock) and the BBC (for the Greenwich 'pips').*

(64) *A satellite navigator supplies the user with accurate latitude and longitude regardless of weather and without any need for calculations.*

(63) *A Decca radio navigator installed in a lifeboat.*

MODERN METHODS OF NAVIGATION

The instruments used for astro-navigation – the sextant, chronometer and almanac – have not changed a great deal except that most chronometers are now quartz rather than clockwork, and all the information required from the almanac is now available from hand-held calculators. The more interesting changes have come from navigational methods that do not depend on the stars.

For many years now it has been possible to navigate the most frequently used sea routes by obtaining your position from radio beacons (63). Originally, the ship's position was found by plotting the *direction* of these beacons, but nowadays it is the relative *distance* to pairs of beacons that is measured. This is done by comparing the phases of the signals transmitted by two beacons, and depends on extremely accurate control of the transmitted signals, since radio waves travel at 300 000 kilometres per second and an error of as little as one ten-thousandth of a second in the transmission time would give an error in position of 30km. This is one of the reasons why a really accurate time service is still needed.

The most exciting recent development is half way to being astronomical, since a satellite is involved: a small box of electronics called SATNAV. This artificial satellite transmits a radio signal at a fixed frequency, but, because of a phenomenon known as the Doppler effect, the frequency appears to be higher when the satellite is approaching you and lower when it is

going away. By measuring this frequency and its rate of change, it is possible to deduce the distance and direction of the satellite. All that is then needed to find your position is a knowledge of the latitude, longitude and altitude of the satellite. Obligingly, it is just this information that is contained in the radio signals that the satellite broadcasts. No calculations are needed; your 'black box' will receive the signal, process it, and immediately present you with your latitude and longitude (64). Just one pass of the satellite gives your position to an accuracy undreamed of by Maskelyne or Harrison, and a few days of satellite measurements can specify the position to within a few metres.

Despite the ease and accuracy of these electronic methods of navigation, they depend on radio signals which could easily be jammed by an enemy in time of war. For this reason there will always be a need for the traditional tools and skills of the navigator.

To complete the story, there are yet more accurate observatory-based methods of finding position on land. These use such techniques as VLBI (Very Long Baseline Interferometry), or laser ranging by timing how long it takes to bounce a flash of laser light off a reflector on the Moon or on an artificial satellite. By these methods it is possible to measure positions to within a few centimetres. At this level of accuracy it is found that, as well as being an imperfect timekeeper, the Earth is also an imperfect position keeper. The continents are moving relative to one another, so not even latitude and longitude remain constant.